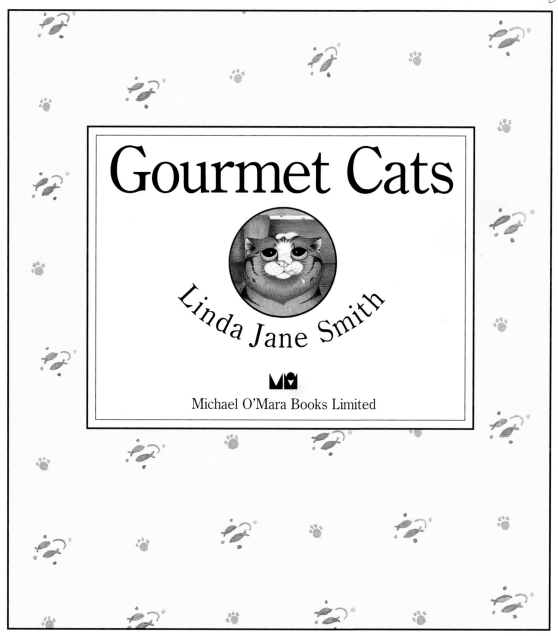

Gourmet Cats

Linda Jane Smith

Michael O'Mara Books Limited

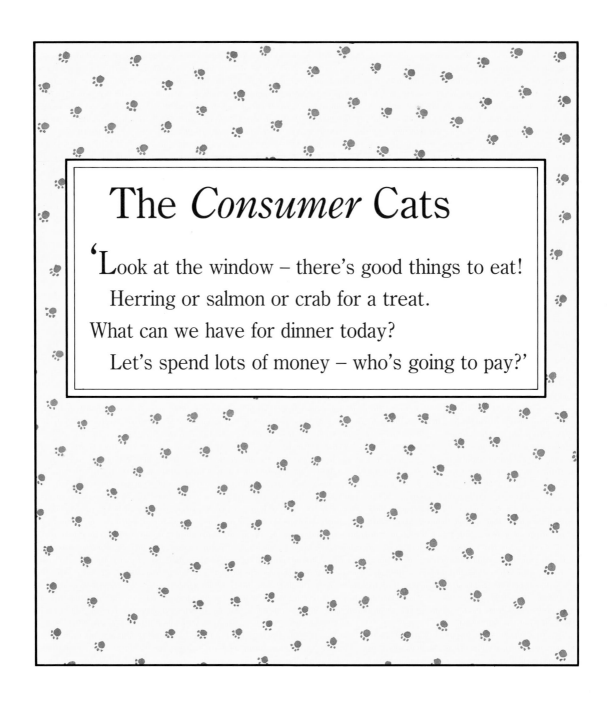

The *Consumer* Cats

'Look at the window – there's good things to eat!
Herring or salmon or crab for a treat.
What can we have for dinner today?
Let's spend lots of money – who's going to pay?'

3

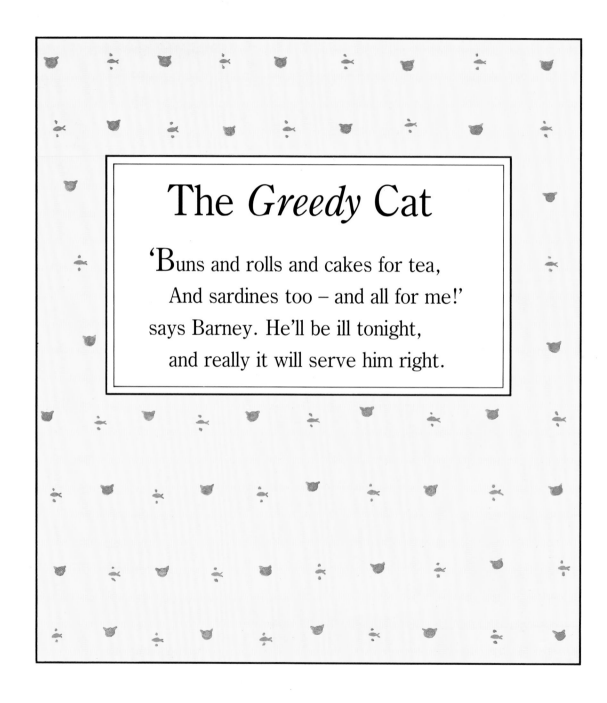

The *Greedy* Cat

'Buns and rolls and cakes for tea,
   And sardines too – and all for me!'
says Barney. He'll be ill tonight,
   and really it will serve him right.

Privileged Cat

Madam Fluff is nobly bred,
   Has breakfast on a tray in bed,
With soft-boiled egg and toast and tea.
   What comfort! Oh, what luxury!

The *Party* Cats

Party cats are most polite.
　　They never yowl, they never fight,
But Tom forgot this and he threw
　　A cream cake at a cat he knew.
Splat! went the cream. Now it is plain
　　That Tom will not be asked again.

The *Fat* Cat

Says Rollo, 'I'm cunning – when no one's about,
I'll feed on the best, such as salmon and trout.
The larder is groaning with good things to eat –
I'm the fattest and happiest cat in the street!'

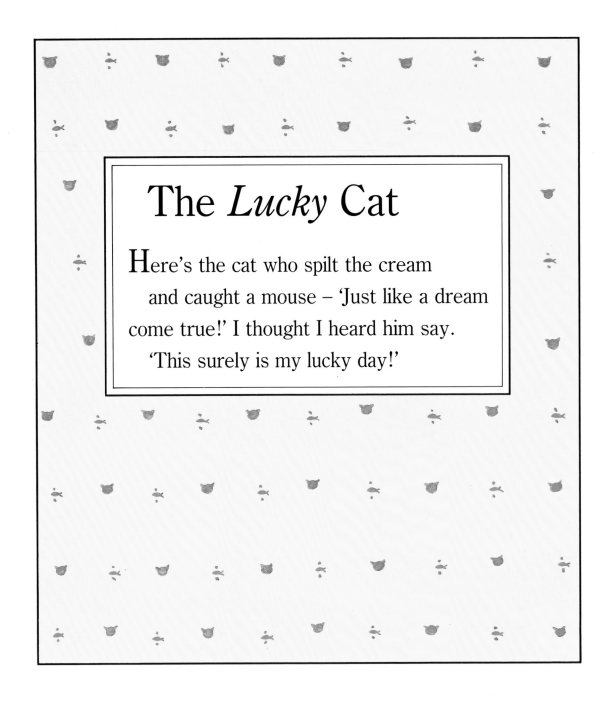

The *Lucky* Cat

Here's the cat who spilt the cream
  and caught a mouse – 'Just like a dream
come true!' I thought I heard him say.
  'This surely is my lucky day!'

The *Kitty* Cats

They sit beside their empty plates.
Each hungry kitten, hopeful, waits
With patience, but they seem to say
'What's on the menu today?'

15

The *Ambitious* Cat

Timmy, prowling, found a feast –
   Whole roast chicken! 'Well, at least,
This will make a bite for lunch.'
   Licked his lips, began to munch.
Soon felt full, and halfway through
   He'd bitten more than he could chew.

16

17

The *Courting* Cats

Bella and Bonzo are as close as can be,
They never fall out, and they always agree
On sharing their meal, and on when they will sup.
There's plenty for both, and less washing up!

18

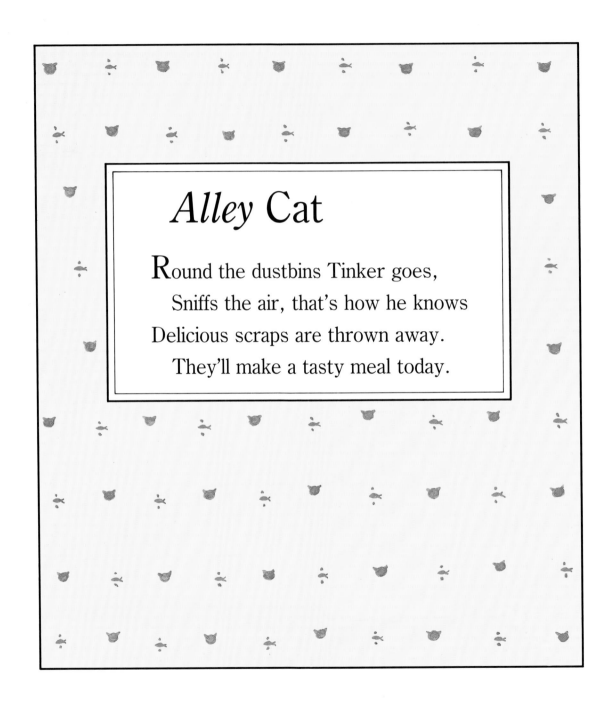

Alley Cat

Round the dustbins Tinker goes,
Sniffs the air, that's how he knows
Delicious scraps are thrown away.
They'll make a tasty meal today.

20

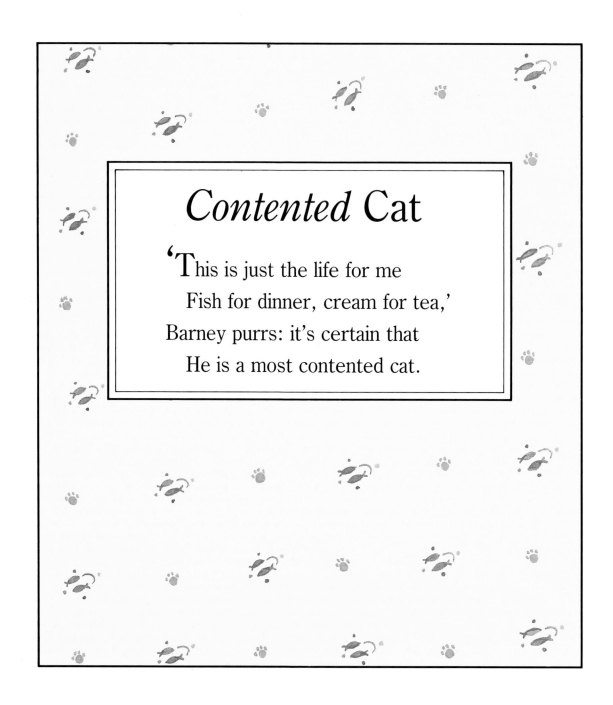

Contented Cat

'This is just the life for me
Fish for dinner, cream for tea,'
Barney purrs: it's certain that
He is a most contented cat.

The *Naughty* Cat

One day, Tam's owner wasn't there.
He jumped upon the table where
He found a feast, and all for free.
He broke the eggs and spilt the tea,
He tried the cake mix, licked the jam,
'Oh, what a clever cat I am!'

24

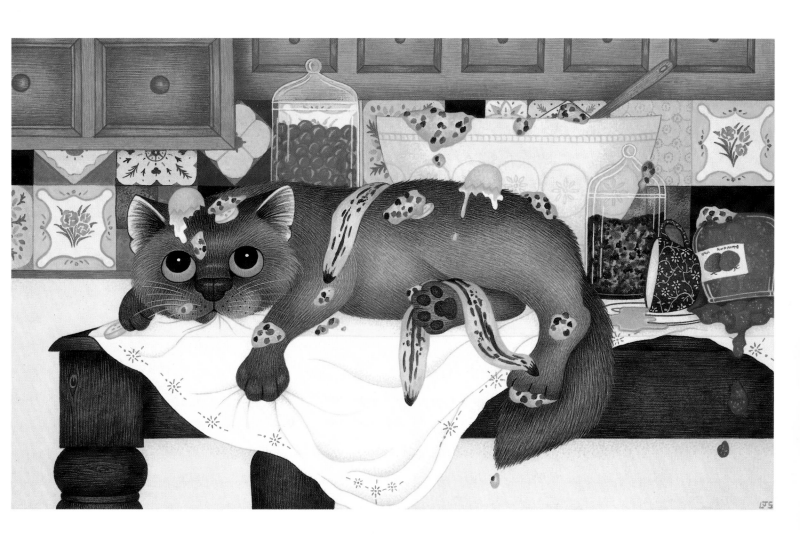

25

The *Gourmet* Cats

We turn up our noses at herring and sprats,
Because we are both epicurean cats,
With lobster and salmon as everyday fare,
It has to be said we're a fortunate pair!

27

The *Frustrated* Cat

Two fat goldfish – what a sight!
  Sure they'd make a tasty bite
Toby's watching, hoping, waiting –
  Can't get at 'em. How frustrating!

28

29

The *Festive* Cats

Christmas dinner – what a spread!
'Come and share it,' Tibby said.
With crackers, paper hats and fun.
There's plenty here for everyone!
And after we have cleared away,
We'll go to sleep till Boxing Day.

First published in 1993 by
Michael O'Mara Books Limited,
9 Lion Yard, Tremadoc Road, London SW4 7NQ

A CIP catalogue record for this book is available from the British Library

ISBN 1-85479-151-6 (hardback)
ISBN 1-85479-142-7 (paperback)

Design: Simon Bell

Typeset by Florencetype Ltd, Kewstoke, Avon
Printed and bound in Hong Kong by Paramount Printing Group Limited